Dear Tomorrow

JOURNALING YOUR
STORY TODAY

NINA HUNDLEY

Cover & interior design by Typewriter Creative Co.
Cover art by West Wind Creative on CreativeMarket.com

ISBN 978-1-7368959-0-0 (Paperback)

This journal is dedicated to Dean and Debbie Brooks, faithful legacy builders who showed me what it's like to focus on the important things in life.

Introduction

Most of us want to make our lives count for something greater than ourselves. We want to share our successes, our highs and lows with those we love. We want to say, "This is the moment that changed my life," and "Here's a lesson you can take away from what I experienced."

Why don't we do that right now?

I am a huge fan of the phrase, "share your story." After giving birth to my first child, I started writing down words of wisdom I wanted to share with my son one day. But realistically, I did not have a lot of time. A legacy journal was out of the question, and because I was so exhausted, I wanted something short and impactful. So I created this journal.

Maybe you think you don't have a story. Maybe you think you wouldn't know what to say if you do. I'd like to introduce you to a different type of journal—one with short, concise questions that you can answer right now, not in the distant future. The dreams you have, the pivotal moments in life that stand out and define you as you are in this moment—they can be recorded now and for generations to come.

This journal is made not only for you, but for those around you and those who come behind you. My hope is that you realize who you are and who you want to be, while sharing those stories—those truths—with others around you.

Sometimes it's easy to say words of wisdom or share life

lessons, and sometimes it's not. Let this simple journal preserve those conversations for you. Share them with a new graduate, a friend starting a new job, or a family member you want to know certain things about you. Keep it for yourself on a day you want to revisit how far you have come. This journal will make an excellent gift for special moments in your life.

I long to see this resource impact a student's life or a relationship where it's hard to get the words out. I long to see it grow a person in ways that only pondering the purposes of life can. Maybe it will provide healing or determination. Perhaps it will lead to open doors or an awareness of identity.

Ultimately, I hope this journal creates purpose. I want you to see how much purpose you have, own your abilities and accomplishments, and share that willingly with others. In a couple of years when you've grown some more, come back and share what you've learned again.

Sharing any part of your story is a gift that reaches further than you could ever imagine.

Journaling Your Story Today

Reflect

In what ways have you made a difference?

*Let this be as broad or specific as you'd like. Consider ways
you have (and ways you are currently) making a difference.*

Respond

_____

_____

_____

_____

_____

_____

_____

_____

_____

_____

_____

_____

_____

_____

_____

Reflect

Have there been social or cultural events
in your life that changed you?

*Consider the ways it impacted you. Did it
change things for better or for worse? How did
it affect you? Did it propel you forward?*

Respond

Reflect

What have you accomplished that impacted
someone or something around you?

Think of all your accomplishments in life.
What are those that affected your career, family,
community, etc.? Write them all here.

Respond

_____

_____

_____

_____

_____

_____

_____

_____

_____

_____

_____

_____

_____

_____

_____

Reflect

What is the one thing you want
someone to learn from your life?

Narrow it down to one thing here.

Respond

Reflect

Was there a particular life event or
moment that shaped you?

*Think about a life event such as a move, birth, job,
loss, decision, or a relationship as an example.*

Respond

Reflect

How did others impact your life?

*Perhaps it is someone currently impacting your life. Consider
the influence of those around you—a mentor, friend,
pastor, family member, etc. Did they have a positive or
negative impact? What have you learned from them?*

Respond

Reflect

What is something you would tell your younger self?

What important advice would you share?

Respond

_____

_____

_____

_____

_____

_____

_____

_____

_____

_____

_____

_____

_____

_____

_____

Reflect

What are truths about your life you are willing to share?

*What is a truth you have learned or you are currently
learning? What is a truth you want to pass on?*

Respond

_____

_____

_____

_____

_____

_____

_____

_____

_____

_____

_____

_____

_____

_____

_____

_____

_____

Reflect

What is a hardship or challenge you faced?

Because life is full of hills and valleys, consider your valley here. What are the key takeaways and lessons learned? Perhaps you are in that valley now. What is your perspective?

Respond

_____

_____

_____

_____

_____

_____

_____

_____

_____

_____

_____

_____

_____

_____

_____

_____

Reflect

What decision do you want to make for the future?

Who do you want to be? What do you want to say?

Respond

More to Say

More to Say

More to Say

More to Say

Words of Wisdom

"Let the most beautiful story you ever tell
be the life you lived abundantly."

—Arielle Estoria

"Don't judge each day by the harvest you
reap, but by the seeds that you plant."

—Robert Louis Stevenson

"One today is worth two tomorrows; what
I am to be, I am now becoming."

—Benjamin Franklin

"Success is liking yourself, liking what
you do, and liking how you do it."

—Maya Angelou

"People who really want to make a difference in the
world usually do it, in one way or another. And I've
noticed something about people who make a difference
in the world: They hold the unshakable conviction
that individuals are extremely important, that every life
matters. They get excited over one smile. They are willing
to feed one stomach, educate one mind, and treat one
wound. They aren't determined to revolutionize the
world all at once; they're satisfied with small changes."

—Beth Clark

"We must use time creatively, in the knowledge
that the time is always ripe to do right."

—Martin Luther King, Jr.

"Life is a matter of choices, and every
choice you make makes you."

—John Maxwell

Your words matter.

Acknowledgements

A word of sincere appreciation to Caleb and Elias, loves of my life. Casey Hilty, Christina Vaughn, Twyla Franz, Lisa Appelo, Charity Rios, Taryn Nergaard, Sara Ward, and my Hope Writers crew. Anything I write is always for You, Jesus.

About the Author

Nina Hundley has been published in the medical community, various faith blogs, and The Joyful Life Community. She is a freelance editor and a member of The Christian PEN, Editorial Freelance Association, Hope Writers, and American Christian Fiction Writers. Nina publishes a monthly newsletter with book reviews and hope-filled content. She writes short stories of hope on her blog, and welcomes visitors to sign up at: www.NinaHundley.com.

Made in the USA
Monee, IL
07 May 2021

66943069R00022